Beautiful bedtime stories

with **Mary**

Beautiful bedtime stories with Mary: Published 2014
by The Incorporated Catholic Truth Society
40-46 Harleyford Road, London SE11 5AY
Tel: 020 7640 0042; Fax 020 7640 0046
www.CTSBooks.org

Translated from the French edition by
Helena Scott

ISBN : 978-1-78469-017-5

CTS Code CH57

Translated from the original French language edition,
Belles histoires pour s'endormir avec Marie,
written by Charlotte Grossetête and illustrated by
Madeleine Brunelet, Sibylle Delacroix,
Dominique Mertens and Eric Puybaret

ISBN : 978-2-72891-712-9

Beautiful bedtime stories

with **Mary**

Text by Charlotte Grossetête
Illustrated by Madeleine Brunelet,
Sibylle Delacroix,
Dominique Mertens
and Eric Puybaret

CTS Children's Books

Contents

Mary's childhood

That morning, when Joachim came home from the Temple, his wife Anne could see straight away that he was sad. They had been married for such a long time that she could read Joachim's feelings in his face. "What's wrong?" she asked. Joachim hesitated before answering, because he did not want to make his wife sad too. But in the end he said, "The High Priest has sacked me. He doesn't want me to be one of the priests in the Temple any more." "But why?" exclaimed Anne. "Because we haven't been able to have any children," answered Joachim. "He thinks that means God has cursed us."

Anne was a strong, brave woman, but at those words she burst into tears. "It's not fair to say things like that!" she sobbed. "I'm certain that God loves us. We've always served him faithfully, as well as we could. And his love is infinite." Joachim hugged her to his heart to comfort her, and then said with a sigh, "I'm going to go and spend some time in the desert. I need to pray. In the silence of the desert, you feel closer to God." Joachim did as he had said. He spent forty days alone in the desert, praying from morning to night. His heart was heavy, but he called on God's help with trust and confidence.

After forty days an angel appeared to him. "Joachim," said the angel, "the Lord has heard your prayer, and also the prayer of Anne, who is praying to him at home, day and night. How right you were to believe in his love! You are blessed: you will soon have a child, a little girl who will be different from anyone else, with a very special destiny in store for her."

After the angel had gone, Joachim hurried back home to Jerusalem. Just as he reached the Golden Gate, the entrance to the city, Anne came running to meet him and threw herself into his arms. They were so happy to be together again!

Some time later they had a little girl, and they called her Mary. When the High Priest heard that Anne had given birth, he called Joachim to the Temple and, looking rather embarrassed, said, "I'm sorry I sacked you. Please come back and join us again." The other priests all nodded, and one of them said, "We've been missing you! You have always been a wonderful servant of God and an example to the rest of us."

Time went by. Mary grew without ever causing her parents any trouble or worry. She was never selfish, and never got cross. She was a lively, funny child, sometimes mischievous, but always as kind as could be. It seemed as though there was not even the tiniest hint of anything bad in her heart.

Sometimes, to Anne's surprise, she saw that her little daughter would stay in her room for hours at a time. Then she would walk quietly round the outside of the house and glance in at the window. She saw Mary on her knees, concentrating so hard on praying to God that she had forgotten everything else.

One day, Anne said to Joachim, "How happy it makes me to see that Mary is so close to God! You can see our little girl is a gift from Heaven." Joachim answered, "By praying, she is preparing her heart for the very special destiny the angel told us about." "Yes," said Anne thoughtfully. "When I see her looking so absorbed, as still as a stone – "

Just then Mary rushed into the house like a whirlwind. "Well, I never knew stones could run that fast!" laughed Joachim. "What's the hurry, Mary? What do you want?" "It's time for our visit to the poor, Daddy! Are you coming?". Joachim got up willingly. Every afternoon, they went to give food to poor people together. Before Mary was born, Joachim used to go round by himself. Now he always took his daughter with him – or rather she dragged him along, wanting to go further and spend longer each time they went. It was a favourite walk for both of them.

Anne gave Mary the basket of food she had prepared, and smiled as she watched them set off. "Don't tire your poor old father out!" she called as they turned the corner. "Yesterday he came back exhausted!" Mary turned round. "I promise, Mummy!" she said, waving. Anne waved back, thinking, "She really is full of grace, that child!"

The Annunciation

After Anne and Joachim settled in Nazareth, more than one of the young men from the village came and asked them for Mary's hand in marriage. Mary had grown into a very beautiful girl, and when she went to the well to draw water, people would turn and look at her as she went by. Not only her beauty, but especially her sweetness and her lovely smile, charmed everyone's heart.

In the end, Joachim and Anne accepted the offer of marriage made by Joseph, the carpenter, who seemed to them to be the best man to be Mary's fiancé. Firstly, because he loved God with all his soul; and secondly – though this was less important in Anne's and Joachim's eyes – because he was descended from King David.

Mary was very happy with her parents' choice for her. Joseph was a tall, strong young man, as solid as the wood he worked with, and she felt she could love and trust him. She was quite sure they would be very happy together, in the sight of God.

One morning she was busy sewing some linen for their future home. She had just put the lamp out, because the dawn was flooding the room with light. As she worked, Mary could hear the birds waking up the countryside, and she thought about her beloved Joseph. "In a little while I'll go and visit him at his workshop," she told herself.

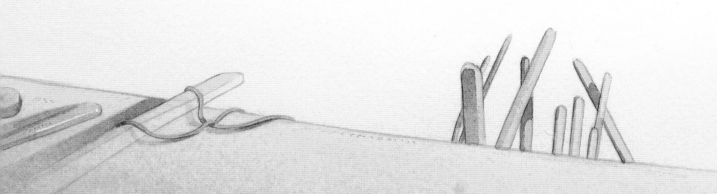

Suddenly she felt there was someone standing in her room, someone who hadn't come through the door, someone she hadn't heard arriving. She looked at his face, which shone with light, and all at once she realised it was an angel. "Rejoice, full of grace, the Lord is with you," said the Angel Gabriel, bowing down before the young girl.

Astonished, Mary dropped her needle. God's messenger continued: "Don't be afraid, Mary, for you have found favour with God. You will have a son, and you will call him Jesus." Mary's face showed her immense surprise. "How can I have a son? I'm not yet married." The Angel Gabriel replied, "The Holy Spirit will come upon you, and the power of the Most High will cover you with its shadow. Therefore the Holy One to be born of you will be called the Son of God."

As Mary remained silent, the angel added, "Your cousin Elizabeth, the one everyone calls barren, is going to have a son too, in spite of her old age, because nothing is impossible for God!" Then Mary said, "I am the handmaid of the Lord. Let what you have said be done to me."

The angel disappeared. Mary sat there for a while longer, meditating on what had happened and saying to God again, "Yes, I accept." Then she thought of her fiancé and got up to go and see him. But once outside the house, she was suddenly filled with anguish. "How can I explain this to Joseph? What will he think when he hears that I'm expecting a baby? God is the only one who can tell him the news!"

So she changed her mind. Leaving Nazareth, she set off as fast as she could to the hill-country where Elizabeth and her husband Zachary lived. She needed to talk to her cousin about the miracle that had happened to them both.

When she reached Elizabeth's house, she gave her a big hug. She could see that Elizabeth was indeed expecting a baby. Elizabeth was very happy and welcomed Mary with a hug in return, saying, "How happy I am that the mother of my Saviour has come to visit me! When you came in, I felt my baby jumping for joy inside me!"

Then a song of joy burst from Mary's lips. "My soul blesses the Lord! He has looked upon his handmaid, he has worked wonders for me! People of all times will call me blessed!"

Mary stayed with Elizabeth and Zachary for some time. She often thought about Joseph and was concerned about him. She imagined him being sad or worried that she had gone away. But an angel had appeared to Joseph in a dream and explained everything to him. After that Joseph confidently waited for Mary to come back, filled with awe at the great adventure that God had prepared for them.

The Birth of Jesus

"By order of the Roman Emperor..." When this cry rang out in Nazareth's main square, the villagers ran to hear the message, filled with curiosity. Mary followed them, and was the last to get there because she was careful not run, as her baby would soon be born.

When everyone was silent, the messenger took up his proclamation. "By order of Caesar Augustus, there is to be a census of all the people of the Empire. For this purpose, every man must go and enrol in his native city." Mary turned to look at Joseph, who was also standing there listening to the message, his carpenter's tools in his hand. He looked at her in alarm. His native city was Bethlehem, the City of King David. "Will we really have to travel all that way? What if the baby is born on the journey?" whispered Mary. "I'm afraid so," answered Joseph. "You can't argue with an order from the Emperor."

So Joseph and Mary set off on their journey, through the winter's cold. The road was crowded with people who were also returning to their native towns. The donkey which Joseph had bought for Mary to ride pawed the ground with impatience at the hold-ups. Mary was very tired, but she bravely put up with the slow journey.

At last they came in sight of Bethlehem! Taking the donkey by the bridle, Joseph quickened his pace because night was falling and it was becoming bitterly cold. They needed to find a shelter for the night quickly. Just as they were entering the town, Mary said in a worried voice, "The baby is about to be born."

Joseph went as fast as he could to the only inn in Bethlehem, and knocked firmly at the door. "Who's there?" asked the inn-keeper, opening the door a crack.

"Joseph from Nazareth. I've come to enrol for the census, and –" "You're not the only ones!" exclaimed the inn-keeper. "My inn is full up, people are even sleeping on the floor. Go and find somewhere else to stay." "But my wife is having a baby!" protested Joseph. The inn-keeper shook his head. "Very sorry, but there's just no room at all."

He shut the door again. Joseph and Mary were left alone under the sky twinkling with stars. Joseph put his hand on Mary's shoulder, and said, "Don't worry. I'll find somewhere we can shelter." After searching for a long time, he at last found a stable, open to the winds, in which there was an ox. He spread a bale of straw on the ground and settled Mary there. She smiled at him in gratitude.

In the middle of the night she gave birth to her son Jesus, and wrapped him in swaddling-clothes to protect him from the cold. Then she laid him in the manger for a cradle. Kneeling on the straw, Mary and Joseph contemplated the baby, and their wonder mingled with the peace of the night.

Suddenly the silence was broken by the clatter of footsteps, and sheep baaing. A group of shepherds came hurrying into the stable! The oldest shepherd greeted Mary respectfully, and explained, "An angel appeared to us in the hills where we were watching over our flocks. He announced to us that a Saviour had just been born here. We've come running to see the baby!" At these words the shepherds knelt down before Jesus, while the sheep pressed around the manger. "Shh!" said a little shepherd. "Don't wake the baby!" The sheep kept as still as the men, and the only sound to be heard was the blowing of the ox, who was keeping the baby warm with his breath.

So as to engrave all these events more deeply on her heart, Mary lifted her eyes to the heavens to say "thank you" to God. That was when she noticed a large star approaching from the horizon, as though coming towards Bethlehem. After the shepherds had left, Mary continued to watch the star. Joseph had noticed it too, and evening after evening he examined its progress with great interest. "It's closer than it was yesterday," he said every night.

The mysterious star finally stopped right above Bethlehem. Almost immediately, three travellers in oriental clothes came into the stable. Mary was rocking Baby Jesus in her arms, and he smiled and waved at them, as though he had been expecting a visit from these unknown people.

The magi bowed deeply and placed three gifts at his feet: gold, frankincense and myrrh.

"Thank you," Mary said to them. "It is we who thank you," replied one of the magi, "for bringing into the world a great king to rule over all the earth." The baby who had been born in Bethlehem spent the following years in Nazareth, in his parents' village. Joseph and Mary brought him up lovingly, and Jesus grew in strength and wisdom until he became a man.

The Wedding-feast at Cana

It was a feast day at Cana: two of the young people from the village were celebrating their wedding. The bride, radiant in her wedding-dress, walked among the tables greeting her guests. She stopped by a woman dressed in blue. "Mary!" she exclaimed. "Thank you for coming all the way from Nazareth!" "I'd have come much further than that for such a great day!" replied Mary. "Jesus and I are happy to be here." "Is your son here too, then?" asked the bride. Mary pointed to a man in a white tunic chatting with some friends at a nearby table. "There he is," she said.

"I would never have recognised him!" said the bride. "It's so long since I last saw him." Mary nodded. "He's a grown man now. He's come with some disciples who have been with him for several days." At that moment the man sitting next to Mary, an old man who had already drunk plenty of wine, called out, "More wine, waiter! My glass is empty!"

As the bride moved away, Mary looked at the servant coming to their table. He was looking down into his jug with a worried expression. Why was he looking so concerned, when everyone was happily celebrating? He tipped the jug, but just a few drops of wine came out, and nothing more. "I'm sorry," stammered the servant. "My jug's empty." "Then go and fill it up!" said the old man impatiently. "Yes, yes," said the servant.

He went off. Mary saw him showing his jug to another servant. The musicians had just come to the end of a tune, and she heard the second servant reply: "We have run out of wine! The guests will soon notice."

The music started again, even louder. Then Mary went over to Jesus, who was still talking with his friends. She put her hand on his shoulder and whispered:

"They have no more wine." Jesus looked her straight in the eyes. "Why are you telling me that, Mother? My hour has not yet come." Mary didn't answer, but her beautiful eyes gazed back into his, as if to say, "I know that you can do something." Jesus saw that his friends were intrigued; they were looking at Mary, looking at their empty glasses, and looking at him. Then he got up from the table.

Mary went straight to find the servants. She pointed to Jesus, just as he disappeared behind the house. She told them, "Do whatever he tells you."

The servants ran to catch up with Jesus. He was standing in front of six large, empty stone water-jars. He said to the two men, "Fill these jars with water." The servants hesitated. The job would take some time, and what was the point? But Mary's words had been so clear that they obeyed.

When they finished, Jesus said to them, "Now draw some out, and go and serve it to the master of the feast." The servants went to the high table with a full jug. The master of the feast was busy chatting with the bridegroom and had not yet realised that his glass was empty. He held it out to the servants without looking. As the liquid poured into the glass, the man holding the jug nearly dropped it in surprise. It was wine! The master of the feast tasted it, opened his eyes wide, and turned to the bridegroom. "That's strange," he said. "Normally people serve the best wine first, and when the guests have drunk that, they bring out the wine that's not so good. But you have kept the best wine till the end. I've never tasted such delicious wine! Where were you hiding it?"

The servants were dying to say what had happened, but Jesus put his finger to his lips. "Shh!" he said. Then the master of the feast raised his glass. "Long life to the newly-weds, and may their happiness be as perfect as this extraordinary wine!"

Everyone clapped. The servants set to work filling everyone's glasses, they were no longer worried and were able to share in the general rejoicing. Yes, everyone was very, very happy!

"Mother, this is your son"

Mary was standing at the foot of the cross. It was the saddest day of her life. Her son was dying. Raising her head, she could see Jesus's face looking down at her and at the world. With his hands stretched out, he seemed to be embracing the whole of the earth before going back to his Father. He was about to give his life for love, as Mary knew.

But it was so cruel! She remembered the morning when she had presented her baby in the Temple at Jerusalem. An old man named Simeon had taken Jesus in his arms, announcing that this was to be the Saviour of all humankind. Then he had said to Mary, "One day, you will suffer greatly for your child. A sword of sorrow will pierce your heart." On that terrible Friday, Simeon's words came true. Mary's pain reached the very depths of her soul. But she knew that God's love and God's blessing were even greater than death.

Tearing her eyes away from Jesus, Mary saw the crowd gathered in front of the cross. There were some stern-looking soldiers, and some of Jesus's enemies who had come to see him die. But most people were crying, because they knew that Jesus had done nothing wrong. Mary recognised people who had been blind, sick, or paralytic, whom her son had cured, and even people he had raised from the dead. She thought, "Who will dare to say aloud that my son's execution is unjust?" Just then a voice cried out, "I deserve my punishment, but this man is innocent. Jesus, remember me when you are in your Kingdom!" Mary looked up at the person who had spoken. It was a thief who had been crucified next to her son. He was the only one who was not afraid to tell the truth – he had already been sentenced to death.

Mary turned away from the crowd and looked at John, Jesus's best friend, who was standing beside her. All the other disciples were hiding a long way away for fear of being arrested. But John had said to Mary, "There's no way I'm going to desert your son, even if I die for it." John had kept his word. After Jesus's trial, he had offered Mary his arm and supported her all the way to the top of Calvary. Thanks to him, Mary felt a little less alone when Jesus was leaving them.

Suddenly there came a cry from the cross. "Mother..." Mary lifted her eyes, astonished. "Mother, this is your son," said Jesus, pointing at John with his chin. Then he added, "And John, this is your mother."

John's eyes widened. For the first time since Jesus was arrested, Mary saw in them a spark of hope. Now John knew that life was going to go on, because Jesus was entrusting his own mother to him. Mary looked at him tenderly. She understood perfectly what her son meant. By asking her to adopt this young, bewildered disciple, Jesus was asking her to become the mother of all men and women.

In the middle of the afternoon, it suddenly got dark. A last cry came from the cross. "Father, into your hands I commend my spirit!" Jesus had just died. Mary took John's hand and squeezed it hard. They waited until Jesus's body had been taken down from the cross, and together they accompanied it to the tomb. Then John took Mary home, and they both prayed through the hours of night and silence.

On Sunday morning, some friends of Mary knocked at the door and then ran straight in, trembling with excitement. "We've just come from the cemetery. Jesus's tomb is empty! An angel told us that he has risen!" At these words, John ran to the cemetery, leaving Mary in the house, to find out if this good news was true and tell her as soon as possible. When he came back, his eyes shone with light. "Mother!" he said. "I saw an angel too! He announced to me that Jesus has overcome death. Your son really has risen! He is alive!"